The Bathroom Game Book

By

Russ Edwards and Leona Balcezak

RED-LETTER PRESS, INC.
SADDLE RIVER, NEW JERSEY

THE BATHROOM GAME BOOK

Copyright © 1987 Red-Letter Press, Inc.
ISBN: 0-940462-06-0
All rights reserved
Printed in the United States of America

For information address Red-Letter Press, Inc.,
P.O. Box 393, Saddle River, N.J. 07458

Introduction

Russ Edwards and Leona Balcezak have finally come out of the water closet where they've been brainstorming for showers on end over *The Bathroom Game Book*. As a result, the authors have created a veritable potty-of-plenty to stimulate bathroom thinking.

It is in the spirit of things that this introduction is presented. Get into the swing of this book by doing some preliminary puzzle work right here. Easy does it. All you have to do is come up with the initial letter from each sentence on this page. Mix the letters into the proper sequence and presto - you've discovered how *The Bathroom Game Book* authors got together.

Russ and Leona advise that if you can't figure this one out you might as well hit the shower because, with the stuff they have in store, you'll undoubtedly be taking a bath.

Jack Kreismer,
Publisher

(Answer - *The first letters of each sentence unscramble to spell the solution - marriage.*)

The Bathroom Game Book

The Bathroom Library™

The John

Well, we might as well get started and go right into the john. This quiz tests your knowledge of "johns" in history and popular culture. The clues suggest a name or phrase that includes some form of "john." Students, sharpen your pencils and take your seats. . .

1. Willowy Walton _____

2. A real pill _____

3. Ed's intro _____

4. Generic citizen _____

5. On the dotted line _____

6. Planting pioneer _____

7. Unidentified person _____

8. Dudley Do-Right's undoing _____

9. "Playin' his guitar just like ringin' a bell"

    _____

10. Merry man _____

Potty-pourri

What month, aside from February, is the shortest?
loses an hour - commonly April.
The month Daylight Savings Time goes into effect -

1. *John Boy.*

2. *Upjohn.*

3. *He-e-e-e-e-e-e-e-r-e's Johnny!*

4. *John Q. Public.*

5. *John Hancock.*

6. *Johnny Appleseed.*

7. *John Doe.*

8. *Dishonest John.*

9. *Johnny B. Goode.*

10. *Little John.*

Potty-pourri

What state name in capital letters is the same upside-down in a mirror?

`OIHO`

Brain Drain

You're fairly smart, right? You know shinola from a hole in the ground, don'tcha? Well then, this quiz should be like taking candy from a fish in a barrel...

1. How many grooves are in a standard 45 R.P.M. "single" record?

2. As I was going to St. Ives, I met a man with seven wives. Seven wives had seven sacks, seven sacks had seven cats, seven cats had seven kits. Kits, cats, sacks and wives— how many were going to St. Ives?

3. According to Scripture, how many of each type of animal did Moses take on the Ark with him?

4. 22% of the phone numbers in Chicago are unlisted. If you picked 700 numbers at random from the phone book, how many unlisted numbers would you expect in your sample?

5. Brothers and sisters I have none but "this man's" father is my father's son. Who is "this man?"

6. Brian has two general circulation United States coins in the pocket of his overalls. Together, they total thirty cents— but one is not a nickel! What coins does he have?

7. Is there biological justification for a man not marrying his widow's sister?

1.   *Just two. One on one side; one on the flip side.*

2.   *One. Only "I" was going to St. Ives.*

3.   *None. Moses missed the boat— there was Noah room anyway.*

4.   *Zero. Unlisted numbers aren't published in phone books.*

5.   *"This man" is the speaker's son.*

6.   *The one that is not a nickel is a quarter; the other is a nickel.*

7.   *Plenty! For starters, the honeymoon would be dead-ly dull. . .*

Potty-pourri

Mr. Byamile, head of the Science Department at Falootin' High, entered Ms. Begotten's third-period chemistry class and requested a momentary conference in the hall. In order to keep the young Einsteins from whipping up some weapons-grade uranium in her absence, he wrote the formula H I O Ag on the blackboard and asked them to translate it into common English. Quick-for extra credit— what is it?

Hi-O Silver!

Perry Maison:
Case of the Cringing Cat

Famed criminal lawyer/vintner Perry Maison— "He will solve no crime before it's time"— was in for a shock when he entered the vineyard guest house and found Paul and Della dead on the floor. Instead of popping his cork, he maintained a professional detachment as his trained eye scanned the room for clues. He noted his cat, Hamburger, was cowering in a corner, nervously licking his front paws. Kneeling down and finding that the carpet around the bodies was wet, Maison immediately deduced the victims had died of suffocation. Perry Maison now knew the killer's identity. Having solved the crime, Maison allowed himself to feel grief. He sadly picked up an overturned bowl from the floor and filled it to the brim with his finest white wine and began toasting Paul and Della's memory. He somehow never quite got around to calling Lt. Drag. How did he figure it out?

Potty-pourri

Two men are playing Trivial Pursuit. They play three games and each win the same number of times yet none of the games is a draw or a default. For a bathroom wedgie, how'd that happen?

They weren't playing each other.

1.   *Paul and Della were goldfish.*

Potty-pourri

We didn't planet this way: Jupiter's volume is over a thousand times greater than Earth's. The Jovian world is about five times as far from the sun as Earth and its diameter is about ten times Earth's. Which takes longer, a day on Jupiter or a day on Earth?

A day on Earth—almost twenty-four hours compared to less than ten hours for a Jupiter day.

Sound Spectrum

The following groups of recording artists have all had hit songs with colors in the titles. For each group, name the color and the songs.

1.

Kermit the Frog
Sgt. Barry Sadler
Helen O'Connell
O. C. Smith

2.

The Cyrkle
Helen Reddy
1910 Fruitgum Company
Gene Autry

3.

The Beatles
Tony Orlando & Dawn
Brian Hyland
Donovan

4.

Cream
Procol Harum
Bing Crosby
Moody Blues

5.

Horst Jankowsky
Los Bravos
Rolling Stones
Hollies

6.

Bruce Springsteen
Dodie Stevens
Perez Prado
Marty Robbins

Answers

1. GREEN

*It's Not Easy Being
   Green.
Ballad of the Green
   Berets.
Green Eyes.
Little Green Apples.*

2. RED

*Red Rubber Ball.
Ruby Red Dress.
1-2-3 Red Light.
Rudolph the Red Nosed
   Reindeer.*

3. YELLOW

*Yellow Submarine.
Tie a Yellow Ribbon
   'Round the Ole
   Oak Tree.
Itsy Bitsy Teenie Weenie
   Yellow Polkadot Bikini.
Mellow Yellow.*

4. WHITE

*White Room.
A Whiter Shade of Pale.
White Christmas.
Nights In White Satin.*

5. BLACK

*A Walk in the Black
   Forest.
Black is Black.
Paint it Black.
Long Cool Woman in a
   Black Dress.*

6. PINK

*Pink Cadillac.
Tan Shoes with Pink
   Shoelaces.
Cherry Pink & Apple
   Blossom White.
A White Sport Coat and A
Pink Carnation.*

Phrase Craze

See if you can figure out what phrases these items represent.

1.   <u>EGGS</u>
          EASY

2. | R | E | A | D | I | N | G |

3.   TIMING
          TIM   ING

4.   <u>FIDDLER</u>
          THE ROOF

5.   SEASONS
          SEASONS
          SEASONS
          SEASONS

6.   SOMEWHERE

          THE RAINBOW

7.   ENG LISH

1.   *Eggs over easy.*

2.   *Reading between the lines.*

3.   *Split Second Timing.*

4.   *Fiddler on the Roof.*

5.   *Four Seasons.*

6.   *Somewhere over the Rainbow.*

7.   *Broken English.*

Potty-pourri

How is it possible to travel through any time zone on Earth in just a few seconds?

Move in with Santa at the North Pole or avoid the crowds by going to the South Pole. All the time zones converge at these points and you can even walk into tomorrow.

Switcheroos

This game is a language maze. Start at one word and arrive at another in a given number of steps. You may only change one letter per step and each substitution must result in an actual English word. Slang, proper names and contractions don't count.

Example: Switcheroo PAINT to FLIRT in 3 steps.

PAINT - FAINT - FLINT - FLIRT -- Easy huh?

1.   Switcheroo LINE to TOMB in 4 steps:
            LINE - ___ - ___ - ___ - TOMB

2.   Switcheroo SHOE to FLIP in 5 steps:
            SHOE - ___ - ___ - ___ - ___ - FLIP

3.   Switcheroo WHOLE to SCARE in 4 steps:
            WHOLE - ___ - ___ - ___ - SCARE

4.   Switcheroo MESS to HOST in 4 steps:
            MESS - ___ - ___ - ___ - HOST

5.   Switcheroo SALT to PART in 4 steps:
            SALT - ___ - ___ - ___ - PART

6.   Switcheroo BOOK to COAL in 6 steps:
            BOOK - ___ - ___ - ___ - ___ - ___ - COAL

7.   Switcheroo PLACE to SKATE in 3 steps:
            PLACE - ___ - ___ - SKATE

8.   Switcheroo FLACK to BRASS in 7 steps:
FLACK - ___ - ___ - ___ - ___ - ___ - ___ - BRASS

1.

LINE - LONE - TONE - TOME - TOMB.

2.

SHOE - SHOW - SLOW - SLOP - SLIP - FLIP.

3.

WHOLE - WHALE - SHALE - SCALE - SCARE.

4.

MESS - MASS - MAST - MOST - HOST.

5.

SALT - SALE - PALE - PARE - PART.

6.

BOOK - LOOK - LOOT - MOOT - MOAT - COAT - COAL.

7.

PLACE - PLATE - SLATE - SKATE.

8 .

FLACK - FLASK - FLASH - FLUSH - BLUSH - BRUSH - BRASH - BRASS.

Potty-pourri

What five letter word is pronounced the same even if you amputate four of its letters?

Queue.

It's a Jungle Out There!

Animals hide and lurk everywhere. The following sentences provide cover for several species. See how many you can flush out of the underbrush.
Example: She ha**d Og**den over for dinner. (**DOG**).

1. Mr. Harwood chuckled at the cleverness of <u>The Bathroom Game Book.</u>

2. The hull's dry rot had spread to mast rot and finally, spar rot.

3. The restaurant's Continental ambiance made it a popular eatery.

4. Even during his blue period, the artist preferred to paint on a yellow easel.

5. The alien told Ted Koppel he was leaving Earth because he was tired of oxygen rusting his armpits.

6. The socialite confided that she loved crowds but did quite abhor secluded hideaways.

7. Colonel Gungho shouted at his men, "Blast it! If you're out of ammo, use rocks on the enemy!"

8. A new book about Hitler's months behind bars is called <u>Adolph In The Slammer.</u>

9. As Mrs. Lincoln once said, "Abe aren't you ready yet? We'll be late for the theater!"

10. Much to the chagrin of Pele, phantoms often haunt soccer stadiums.

1. *Mr. Har**wood chuck**led.*

2. *Sp**ar rot.***

3. *Continental **amb**iance - also restaur**ant**.*

4. *Yello**w easel.***

5. *Of **ox**ygen.*

6. *Ab**hor se**cluded.*

7. *Am**mo use.***

8. *A**dolph in.***

9. *A**be ar**en't*

10. ***Pele phant**oms.*

Potty-pourri

Pour substitute: You have a half gallon plastic jug and a gallon plastic jug, each filled with water. You have to put that water into a large wooden barrel but you want to know which water came from which jug. Is there any way to do this?

Yes. Freeze the water in the jugs first and then cut away the plastic before putting the chunks of ice in-to the barrel.

Roundabouts

What goes around, comes around, and this word association game challenges you to complete the circle in exactly five steps. Each word is associated with the words on either side of it. We've given you a letter in its proper position in each word. You may go either way! Good luck!

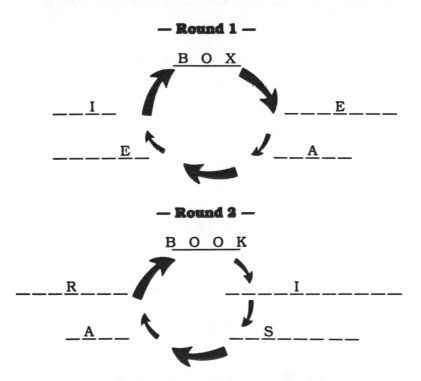

— **Round 1** —

B O X

_ _ I _ _

_ _ _ _ E _ _ _ _

_ _ _ _ _ E _

_ _ A _ _

— **Round 2** —

B O O K

_ _ _ R _ _ _

_ _ _ _ _ I _ _ _

_ A _ _

_ _ S _ _ _ _ _

Round 1:   (CLOCKWISE)

BOX, JEWELRY, CHAIN, LETTER, MAIL.

Round 2:   (CLOCKWISE)

BOOK, APPOINTMENT, BUSINESS, CARD, LIBRARY.

Potty-pourri

Quick Bathroom Cryptogram

OKVNJTTR VWG
ET CTO WD QTEL VWAA VNL GKGLJ
YTJX WD SWEWDNLQ!

*BATHROOM TIP: NO JOB IS DONE
TILL THE PAPER WORK IS FINISHED.*

Alpha-bits

Use the following alpha-bits to fill in the blanks with the words suggested by the clues. The figure in parentheses indicates the number of alpha-bits needed in the answer. Each alpha-bit is used only once.

A, ACK, AD, AM, AN, BA, BL, BO, BR, BU, CES, CK, CRA, CT, CUL, D, DD, DE, DRE, EM, EM, ET, FAM, FE, FRI, ILY, JO, LE, LE, LT, ME, NEY, OCT, OR, OW, PER, PRO, QU, RE, RO, RR, RST, RVE, SA, SAC, SE, SK, SS, STA, TH, TOR, TT, UR, WL

1.	Baby creep.	(2) __ __ __ __
2.	Reverie	(2) __ __ __ __ __
3.	Space ship.	(3) __ __ __ __ __ __
4.	Famish.	(2) __ __ __ __ __
5.	Window shop.	(3) __ __ __ __ __ __
6.	To liquify.	(2) __ __ __ __
7.	A clan.	(2) __ __ __ __ __ __
8.	Physician.	(3) __ __ __ __ __ __
9.	Difficult matter.	(3) __ __ __ __ __ __ __
10.	Trip.	(3) __ __ __ __ __ __ __
11.	Duck cry.	(2) __ __ __ __ __
12.	Glass container.	(3) __ __ __ __ __ __
13.	Made ill at ease.	(5) __ __ __ __ __ __ __ __
14.	To pop.	(2) __ __ __ __ __
15.	Strand.	(3) __ __ __ __ __ __
16.	Forebearer.	(3) __ __ __ __ __ __ __
17.	Search.	(2) __ __ __ __ __
18.	Ideal.	(3) __ __ __ __ __ __ __
19.	Horse's seat.	(3) __ __ __ __ __ __
20.	Blind alley.	(3) __ __ __ - __ __ - __ __ __

Answers

1.   *Crawl.*

2.   *Dream.*

3.   *Rocket.*

4.   *Starve.*

5.   *Browse.*

6.   *Melt.*

7.   *Family.*

8.   *Doctor.*

9.   *Problem.*

10.   *Journey.*

11.   *Quack.*

12.   *Bottle.*

13.   *Embarrass.*

14.   *Burst.*

15.   *Thread.*

16.   *Ancestor.*

17.   *Frisk.*

18.   *Perfect.*

19.   *Saddle.*

20.   *Cul-de-sac.*

Shower Power

Each clue suggests a word or phrase employing some form of "shower" so why not get your feet wet...

1. Presents before you take the plunge _____

2. Loud clouds _____

3. Rain delay _____

4. Douses desire _____

5. Heavenly streakers _____

6. Baseball banishment _____

7. Moist month _____

8. A flurry of activity _____

9. Drapes for drips _____

10. It goes to your head_____

1. *Bridal shower.*

2. *Thundershower.*

3. *Shower stall.*

4. *Cold shower.*

5. *Meteor shower.*

6. *Send to the showers.*

7. *April showers.*

8. *Snow shower.*

9. *Shower curtain.*

10. *Shower cap.*

Potty-pourri

What common household item often displays the fraction "24/31"?

A calendar.

Gullible's Travels

What's your gullibility quotient? This true or false quiz should determine how easily you'll believe even the improbable. A score of ten correct means you have an unusually sharp mind. If you get a zero however, you should immediately contact the publisher and ask about the special Love Canal and Three Mile Island time-share condo offer...

True or False:

1. The greatest height from which a raw chicken egg has been dropped to the ground without breaking is 650 feet.

2. Every day, Americans buy about 200 miles of neckties.

3. During the Civil War, an inexperienced Union officer called a truce in order to ask his Confederate adversaries their advice on military strategy.

4. Joan Collins was once romantically linked with the Shah of Iran but ended the relationship because his excessive passion for television game shows took up the greater part of their time together.

5. Art Carney, TV's Ed Norton, was once the male vocalist with the Horace Heidt Band.

6. The biggest radish ever grown weighed in at 25 pounds.

7. Loose lips might sink ships but Lucy's fillings helped smash a Japanese spy ring in World War II. For some reason, Lucille Ball's dental work picked up their secret radio transmissions and helped the authorities zero in on the operation.

8. The April 30th, 1967 telecast of the Ed Sullivan Show featured Fergie, the Musical Gerbil, and his rendition of *On Broadway* played on a tiny little xylophone.

9. Humphrey Bogart was a ballet dancer in New York City for two years - before having all the toes of his left foot shot off in the First World War.

10. In 1955, the Washington State and San Jose State football teams were forced to play an entire game in wickedly windy, sub-zero cold because one die-hard fan showed up.

1. *True. According to the <u>Guinness Book of World Records</u>, it was dropped by David S. Donoghue onto the Tokyo Golf Course in 1979.*

2. *True. According to Tom Parker's <u>In One Day</u>, that's enough to make about a quarter million of the natty nooses. How many glow in the dark, we don't know.*

3. *True. The battle of Mumfordville, KY was not going well for Col. John T. Wilder, surrounded and out-numbered six to one as he was. To his credit, he sought professional advice. Unfortunately, the only professionals available were Confederates. They allowed that they really couldn't provide him with an objective opinion but that he should consider the dozens of cannons they had trained on his position. He got the point and surrendered.*

4. *False. The Shah is one Joan apparently missed.*

5. *True. But to the everlasting joy of <u>Honeymooners</u> fans, his singing career went down the tubes, right into the sewer.*

6. *True.*

7. *True. However, we're not sure about the story that the leader of the spy ring was quoted as saying, "I hate Rucy!"*

8. *False.*

9. *False. All Bogie's appendages came through the war intact and he never asked for a ballet to be played again Sweetheart.*

10. *True. Although we doubt the fan hung around the locker room door to grab a few autographs after the game.*

Notice Operandi

How observant are you? Would you be able to hold your own in the company of Holmes, Marple and Marlowe? Here's a test to find out:

1. Which major commercial T.V. network uses lower case letters in its logo?

2. In which hand does the Statue of Liberty hold her torch?

3. What are the three colors of the 7-11 sign?

4. What numbers on a phone dial are not accompanied by a segment of the alphabet?

5. How many kilometers per hour is 55 miles per hour?

6. Does the Pillsbury Dough Boy wear a hat?

7. How many wheels of an "eighteen wheeler" are on the trailer?

8. Which side is the hot water faucet usually on?

9. Is Bing Crosby's voice the only one we hear on his famous recording of <u>White Christmas</u>?

10. Which direction is "Whistler's Mother" facing?

1.   *abc.*

2.   *Right.*

3.   *Red, orange and green (often on a white background).*

4.   *1, 0.*

5.   *88 kph.*

6.   *Yes.*

7.   *8.*

8.   *Left.*

9.   *No.*

10.   *Left.*

Potty-pourri

Two mothers and two daughters went on a shopping spree. They bought a cardigan sweater, a pair of designer jeans, and a scarf. Yet they each returned home with one article of clothing: How'd that happen?

Because it was a grandmother, her daughter and her daughter— one of the mothers was also a daughter.

Follow the Dotted Line

1. Using two straight lines make a third arrow.

2. Draw this figure with one continuous line (no retracing).

3. **I O 3 O** Add 3 lines to this number to turn it into a traveling man.

4. | | | | Add 5 marks to make this 10.

5. $VI + II = V$ Can you correct this equation 6 + 2 = 5 by moving one line?

1.

2.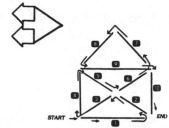

3. $^1\!H$ O $^3\!B$ O

4. TEN

5. *Removing the vertical line of the "PLUS" sign and inserting it immediately after the "EQUAL" sign results in this equation: VI − II = IV*

Potty-pourri

Here's one that goes back a ways: The person who made it had no use for it; the person who bought it didn't want it; and the one who finally ended up with it, never knew about it. What was it?

A Coffin.

Teams Like Old Times

For this quiz, we crank up the way-back machine and set the controls for the Golden Years of Hollywood. You don't have to be a trivia whiz to know about the great teams. Here, names as inseparable as salt and pepper are shuffled together. A more modern example would be RC23DP20 = R2D2/C3PO. The letters are in their proper order, the names are merely combined.

1. BUALRLNESN

2. BBAOCGAARLTL

3. TRHAEPCBURYN

4. ACBOBOSTELTLTO

5. LAHUARREDLY

6. ARSOTGEAIRRES

7. HCOROPSBEY

8. MALERWTIINS

9. LMEATMTHOANU

10. HDUDSAOYN

1. *BURNS/ALLEN.*

2. *BOGART/BACALL.*

3. *TRACY/HEPBURN.*

4. *ABBOTT/COSTELLO.*

5. *LAUREL/HARDY.*

6. *ASTAIRE/ROGERS.*

7. *HOPE/CROSBY.*

8. *MARTIN/LEWIS.*

9. *LEMON/MATTHAU.*

10. *HUDSON/DAY.*

Potty-pourri

History mystery: Who was Thomas Wilson and why was he pretty well known in the early part of the twentieth century?

He happened to be President of the United States for eight years between 1913 and 1921. He preferred to go under his middle name, Woodrow.

Twosy Chewsy Twins

The ad in Variety read as follows: "Major chewing-gum company looking for bright and perky twin sisters— must be identical in appearance— for national ad campaign. Report with picture and resume to Cattlecall Productions, 9AM Monday the 3rd."

Patty and Maxine were thrilled; this could be their big break. No more waitressing in an all night donut shop and getting pinched by the crullers. Fame and fortune awaited.

They figured they were shoo-ins; After all, pert and perky were their specialties.

Bright and bouncy, lithe and lovely, they swept through the audition in an effervescent gush. It was now between them and twins from Pittsburgh named Fiona and Beatrice. They went into their final interview supremely confident.

Mr. Labonza, from the gum company, was to make the final choice:

"Have a seat ladies— in fact— take a couple of them."

Patty and Maxine giggled obligingly.

"Now, in going over your applications and resumes, I notice that you were both born on the same day at the same place to parents of the same names— and you certainly look exactly alike, so I guess it's safe to assume that you are twin sisters."

"Well not exactly, Mr. Labonza. We are sisters..." replied Patty.

"Yes, we are sisters. . ." interjected Maxine, "but we're not twins."

"Not twins?" blustered Labonza. "The Twosy Chewsy Gum Company advertised for twins, we've always had twins and we're not about to change now." Labonza fairly harrumpted them out the door and Fiona and Beatrice became the new Twosy Chewsy Twins.

How could it be possible that Patty and Maxine were not twins?

The sisters were two of a set of triplets.

Potty-pourri

What do the following folk have in common: John Reid, Peter Parker and Don Diego de Vega?

They are all fictitious characters with better known pseudonyms: The Lone Ranger, Spiderman and Zorro.

Logic Boggler

This spring the garden club in our neighborhood donated their prize winning flowers for auctioning. All five members, including Charles and Martha, each contributed one kind of flower which was bought by one of the other members. From the clues given below, can you figure out the full names of each of the five members and the kind of flowers each bought and donated?

1.   The member who donated gladiolus didn't buy roses.

2.   The only member who has the same first and last initials donated the roses.

3.   Martin, who isn't Sandra, donated daffodils and bought violets.

4.   No two members exchanged flowers.

5.   Neither Stevens nor Carmichael donated violets or bought daffodils.

6.   McKennen, who isn't Sandra or Samantha, donated tulips.

7.   Mark isn't Sanders.

FULL NAME	DONATED	BOUGHT
Mark Carmichael	*Gladiolus*	*Tulips*
Samantha Martin	*Daffodils*	*Violets*
Charles McKennan	*Tulips*	*Daffodils*
Martha Sanders	*Violets*	*Roses*
Sandra Stevens	*Roses*	*Gladiolus*

Potty-pourri

There exists on Earth something that has no mass and yet is visible to the naked eye, something that is everyday common but has the ability to lighten any-thing— with the possible exception of objects in water. What is this mystical something?

A hole.

Apples and Oranges

How can you add apples and oranges? Easy, chop 'em up together and make fruit salad. That's sort of the idea behind this quiz. The following equations make no sense until you realize what terms they are dealing with.
Example: $6 + 24 = 1$ (six days plus 24 hours equals one week).

1. $3 + 25 = 1$

2. $144^2 + 8^2 = 1^2$

3. $5290 - 1 = 120$

4. $5 + 5 = 2$

5. $86,400 = 1/7$

6. $1 - 4 = 2$

7. $1 - 1 = 90$

8. $4/7 = 1$

1. *3 quarters plus 25 pennies equal one dollar.*

2. *144 square inches plus 8 square feet equal one square yard.*

3. *5,290 feet minus one mile equals 120 inches.*

4. *5 toes plus 5 toes equal 2 feet.*

5. *86,400 seconds equal 1/7 of a week.*

6. *1 gallon minus 4 pints equal 2 quarts.*

7. *1 century minus 1 decade equals 90 years.*

8. *4 games out of 7 equal one World Series Championship.*

Potty-pourri

Car-tune: What 70's song mentioned a Custom Continental and an Eldorado?

*Jim Croce's **Bad Bad Leroy Brown**.*

Phrase Craze

1.
O
A.A.
B.A.
M.A.
Ph.D.

2.

CIRCUS

3.
GIFT

4.
HAM
RYE

5.
```
        A
  E           P
  S             P
   U         L
        A
```

6. C C C C C C C

1.   *4 degrees below 0.*

2.   *3 ring circus.*

3.   *Gift box.*

4.   *Ham on rye.*

5.   *Round of applause.*

6.   *7 Seas.*

Potty-pourri

A man went into the patent office with a vial of liquid. "I have invented the most powerful acid in the world. This stuff will eat through absolutely anything and I want a patent."

With one look, the clerk refused his request. Why?

His claim had to be false because if the acid ate through anything, how'd he keep it in the vial?

Garbledegooks

Anagram lovers are a special breed. They go into the bathroom to take a thblebubba instead of a bubble bath. And now they can go in the john and happily zupzel away-that's "puzzle" to the rest of us. Unscramble the Garbledegooks for things that you do in the bathroom and then write the boxed letter in the corresponding space at the bottom of the page for an important message. We'll start you off...

1.   u s r c b   s c r u [b] - b goes in space #1

2.   e s w r h o _ _ _ _ [_] _

3.   v s e a h   [_] _ _ _ _

4.   p m u e k a _ _ _ _ - [_] _

5.   s e i r n   [_] _ _ _ _

6.   g e w i h   _ [_] _ _ _

7.   r h l e a t _ _ [_] _ _ _

8.   l y b r o d w _ _ [_] _ - _ _ _

9.   s o f s l   [_] _ _ _ _

10. e g l a g r _ _ _ _ [_] _

11. u h s r b _ _ [_] _ _

12. o h m a o s p [_] _ _ _ _ _ _

13. e b t a h _ _ _ [_] _

IMPORTANT MESSAGE:

B _   _ _ _ _   _ _   _ _ _ _ _ !
1 2   3 4 5 6   7 8   9 10 11 12 13

1.   *Scrub.*
2.   *Shower.*
3.   *Shave.*
4.   *Make-up.*
5.   *Rinse.*
6.   *Weigh.*
7.   *Lather.*
8.   *Blow-dry.*
9.   *Floss.*
10.   *Gargle.*
11.   *Brush.*
12.   *Shampoo.*
13.   *Bathe.*

IMPORTANT MESSAGE:

Be sure to flush!

Tally Ho!

Here's a quickie quiz that will test your arithmetical prowess. Read it through *ONCE* and provide the answer at the end, immediately upon finishing. Don't worry— there's no higher math. If you can count, you can "ace" this one.

The Dogcatcher

Fred Derf, the dogcatcher in Smalltown, started out on his appointed rounds one day with an empty truck. He soon stopped at the park where he nabbed two pooches. Then it was on to the softball field where he parked and flushed out three more. Cruising down Main Street, he spotted four more unlicensed canines, stopped, and caught three of them. Making his usual foot patrol at the dump, he caught a mother poodle and five mongrel puppies but in the confusion of trying to stuff them in the overloaded cage, seven other dogs slipped away. He recaptured one when he stopped at Elmo's for gas and another while he was waiting at a train crossing. Now answer this question: How many stops did Fred make to catch dogs that day?

Six.

Potty-pourri

What common word do SINK and DRIP share as a synonym?

DROP.

In Search Of. . .

```
K  T  O  O  T  H  B  R  U  S  H
O  Q  L  B  P  L  S  T  A  S  R
O  W  E  T  D  A  O  U  P  O  N
B  M  W  K  E  I  O  H  L  L  M
Y  A  O  J  L  C  P  S  U  F  N
C  K  T  E  P  D  U  H  G  S  I
O  E  T  H  R  E  T  A  W  H  A
M  U  E  A  T  A  S  M  F  O  T
B  P  I  Z  P  U  Z  P  U  W  R
K  N  I  S  B  L  B  O  R  E  U
S  E  U  S  S  I  T  O  R  R  C
```

Bathtub	Towel	Toothbrush	Make-up
Shower	Toilet	Comb	Water
Drain	Soap	Floss	Flush
Sink	Shampoo	Curtain	Plug
Faucet	Tissues	Razor	Book

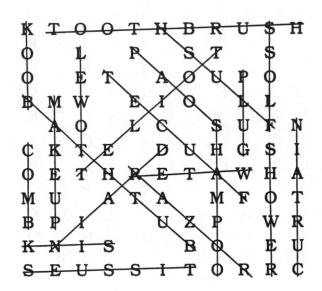

Potty-pourri

What common word do SOLVE and SHAPE share as a synonym?

FIGURE.

Five Easy Pieces

The following ten letter words have been chopped up into five 2 letter chunks. See if you can re as se mb le them.

1.	CH	SS	SP	EE	LE
2.	SI	IS	PE	ON	RM
3.	TA	ES	CA	LO	GU
4.	IZ	CO	GN	RE	ED
5.	LE	OT	GG	BO	ER
6.	GI	MA	TE	LE	TI
7.	HB	NE	OR	IG	LY
8.	PE	NG	WH	RI	IS
9.	ME	TO	NA	NT	UR
10.	VA	GR	NC	IE	ES

1.   *SPEECHLESS.*

2.   *PERMISSION.*

3.   *CATALOGUES.*

4.   *RECOGNIZED.*

5.   *BOOTLEGGER.*

6.   *LEGITIMATE.*

7.   *NEIGHBORLY.*

8.   *WHISPERING.*

9.   *TOURNAMENT.*

10.   *GRIEVANCES.*

Potty-pourri

What is it that occurs once in a second, once in a month, once in a century and yet not at all in a week?

The letter "n".

Roundabouts

Here we go again. . . more free association fun with our not-so-vicious circles. Each word is associated with the words on either side of it and, in order to keep you from going up your tiled walls, we've spotted you a letter in each word.

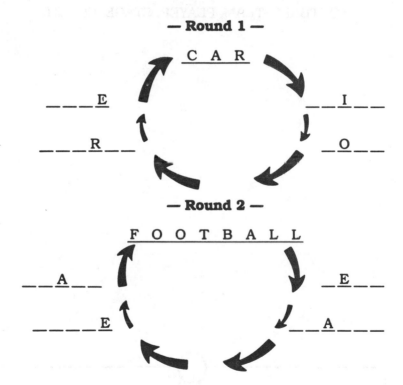

— Round 1 —

C A R

_ _ _ E

_ _ _ R _ _

_ _ _ I _ _

_ O _ _

— Round 2 —

F O O T B A L L

_ _ A _ _

_ _ _ _ _ E

_ E _ _ _

_ _ A _ _ _

Round 1:   (CLOCKWISE)

         CAR, DRIVE, GOLF, COURSE, RACE.

Round 2:   (CLOCKWISE)

         FOOTBALL, TEAM, PLAYER, STAGE, COACH.

Potty-pourri

Memory teaser: What popular song mentions the name of Saint Peter?

Sixteen Tons — "*Saint Peter don'tcha call me 'cause I can't go, I owe my soul to the Company Store*".

The Return of Capt. Smirk

Capt. Smirk of the Starship Booby-prize had spent decades in exile on the planet Syndication. Lately, the only place he had boldly gone where no man had gone before was his accidental foray into the ladies room at the bus station. His pride wounded beyond endurance, he decided to exact revenge from those who caused the premature cancellation of his five year mission— his dreaded enemies, The Neilsens. Upon his arrival on their planet, however, he was captured and sentenced to death— which, all in all, wasn't nearly the indignity that losing his prime time slot to the Brady Bunch was.

The Neilsens, being a rather peculiar race, have a custom of allowing the condemned to indirectly choose the fashion of their demise. Smirk was to make a statement. If it was true, a time-fused phaser would be dropped down his pants; if it was false, he'd be ground up into tribble food. But Smirk hadn't gotten his Captain's insignia for naught. He made a statement which permitted him to continue to jauntily flip his communicator and say *"Beam me up Scotty"*. What was that simple statement which allowed Smirk to live?

He said, "I'll be ground up into tribble food." If the statement was true, then he should have a phaser dropped down his pants. If that happened though, it would make the statement false which would then lead back to it being true once again.

Potty-pourri

Dots Life: What common English word sports three consecutive dotted letters?

Hijinks.

Opposites Attract

In this game, opposites attract too much. They've scrunched and scrambled themselves together into gibberish. See if you can set them straight. . .

Example: ILGWHHO-HIGH/LOW

1. RNRAFEA

2. BOADGOD

3. RTLKDIGAH

4. STQNUIYEOI

5. NTIUO

6. IROPROCH

7. GSKRWOENAT

8. DSBMUTARM

9. PYOCMRMODRAE

10. GYNDHAIT

1.   *NEAR/FAR.*

2.   *GOOD/BAD.*

3.   *LIGHT/DARK.*

4.   *QUIET/NOISY.*

5.   *IN/OUT.*

6.   *RICH/POOR.*

7.   *WEAK/STRONG.*

8.   *SMART/DUMB.*

9.   *ROOMY/CRAMPED.*

10. *NIGHT/DAY.*

Potty-pourri

What is the only letter you wouldn't need to spell the names of all fifty states?

`'..Q..`

In Search Of. . .

See if you can put a lid on this word search by finding all of the bathroom synonyms listed below.

```
    D Q W C I T U
    E S U O H T U O P
  N D P R I V Y R S V Z
I T J L M S L O Y T T O P
R F O E N O C R L P T U E
X E H S O N O P K L T V D
I G N E B T A R U N O R O
C N S B A O U V T L I N M
Q U T V S D N E D S L O M
E O A F L A T R I N E G O
L B A C P N G T D T R C
  Z X O B D N A S N K
    G C F R Y L T W
```

Lavatory	Restroom
Toilet	Latrine
Head	Potty
John	Lounge
Sandbox	Outhouse
Commode	Loo
Can	Privy
WC	

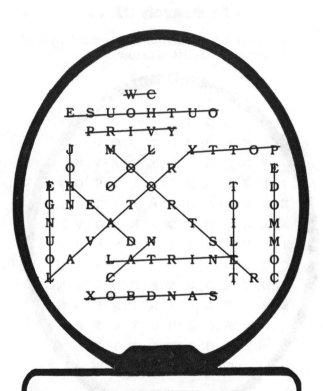

Lavatory   Restroom
Toilet   Latrine
Head   Potty
John   Lounge
Sandbox   Outhouse
    Commode Loo
    Can   Privy
        WC

Headline Hunters

People who write headlines for newspapers are often creatively frustrated and they vent their ire on the rest of the world in the form of puns. Now it's your turn. You're the new headline writer for the <u>Bathroom Mirror</u>. The following phony news "stories" cry out for groaner headlines. All right pun seekers, do your stuff!

Example: Story: Alex Haley announces intention to write book about Lawrence Welk's staid ancestors.
Headline: **ALEX HALEY WRITES SQUARE ROOTS.**

1.   Story: The U.S. Mint intends to coin a commemorative one cent piece honoring a famous one-liner comedian.
       Headline: _____

2.   Story: The President has appointed the former star of television's <u>Dobie Gillis</u> as Ambassador to Spain. However, his arrival in Madrid International Airport spurs such massive demonstrations (It seems that the Spaniards wanted somebody from *Gilligan's Island*.) that Ambassador Hickman was forced to return to his plane.
       Headline: _____

3.   Story: Bruce Springsteen writes a song to honor his favorite Swedish tennis star.
       Headline: _____

4.   Story: A wild golf drive hit by former President Ford seriously injures Juan Valdez of coffee bean fame during a charity golf tournament. Mr. Valdez required twenty stitches to close the wound.
       Headline: _____

5.   Story: A mob-informant held out until the very last minute but then acceded to a plea-bargaining arrangement to turn state's evidence in return for a nine year reduction in his sentence.
       Headline: _____

Note: In this game, closees count.

1.   *HENNY-PENNY ON WAY.*

2.   *DWAYNE IN SPAIN, STAYS MAINLY ON PLANE.*

3.   *SPRINGSTEEN PENS BJORN IN THE USA.*

4.   *JERRY FORD MAKES A HOLE IN JUAN.*

5.   *A SNITCH IN TIME SAVES NINE.*

Potty-pourri

Here's one for the birds: For what type of creatures were the Canary Islands named?

Dogs—"Canary" is a corruption of the Latin "Insularia Canaria," or "Island of Dogs".

Crypto-Riddles

Riddle your brain and try to decode the cryptograms below.

1.   H: LQZE SA WAK RYE VI WAK

           CJABB FAVBAX VGW LVEQ

           Z IAKJ-NYZI CNAGYJ?

    Z: Z JZBQ AI RAAS NKCP.

2.   C:

   HMX ZAF'I IMTX YTI TYTDMPFIK

        AF EPIMUFO ETPRMTK?

    P:

   ETRPGKT IMTX MPST INAGEYT

   VTTDUFO IMTUN INGFVK GD.

1.   *Q:*   *WHAT DO YOU GET IF YOU*
             CROSS POISON IVY WITH
             A FOUR-LEAF CLOVER?
     A: *A RASH OF GOOD LUCK.*

2.   *Q:*

WHY DON'T THEY LET ELEPHANTS
       ON BATHING BEACHES?

     A:

BECAUSE THEY HAVE TROUBLE
KEEPING THEIR TRUNKS UP.

Potty-pourri

What seven letter insect do the British make sport of?

Cricket.

What Kind of Pool am I?

Here's a quiz that should go swimmingly. It's so easy you can't get in over your head so c'mon in— the water's fine!

1.   You can really take a bath in this one:

_____.

2.   This one is rarely behind the eight ball:

_____.

3.   You can really get taken for a ride:

_____.

4.   A real dive:

_____.

5.   It has trouble holding its water:

_____.

6.   These fingers will give you a hand:

_____.

7.   A species' total inheritance:

_____.

8.   You can scratch easily with this:

_____.

9.   Foul play here:

_____.

10.   The grass is always greener over this:

_____.

1. *Office, football, any betting pool.*

2. *Pool shark, hustler.*

3. *Car pool.*

4. *Swimming pool.*

5. *Tidal pool.*

6. *Typing pool.*

7. *Gene pool.*

8. *Pool cue.*

9. *Dirty pool.*

10. *Cesspool.*
    (A tip of the toilet seat to Erma Bombeck for this one.)

Potty-pourri

What word is spelled wrong, no matter which dictionary you look it up in?

W-r-o-n-g.

Notice Operandi

Here we go again! How observant are you? Hopefully, after the last test, you've been practicing. Let's see if you've improved.

1. In top to bottom traffic lights, which color is on the bottom?

2. Which way does Lincoln face on a penny?

3. What does it say in smaller print just under the title of *Playboy* magazine?

4. What number is at the extreme right-hand end of the AM radio dial?

5. Which way does the RCA dog face to hear his master's voice?

6. Which way does the printing run on a standard pencil —towards the point or away?

7. Are there more red stripes or white stripes on the American flag?

8. On a five dollar bill, there are a total of eight corners. How many of those corners contain the numeral 5?

9. Without looking - what's the name of this quiz?

10. What letters of the alphabet have been omitted from the phone dial?

1. *Green.*

2. *Right.*

3. *"Entertainment for Men."*

4. *16 (1600).*

5. *Left.*

6. *Away.*

7. *The reds win 7 to 6.*

8. *6-two others say FIVE.*

9. *Notice Operandi.*

10. *Q, Z.*

Potty-pourri

A really big shoe: In what common sport are all metal shoes used.

Horse racing — or horseshoe pitching.

Logic Boggler

The Pitney Pineys were on a roll at the basketball game. They wiped out the other team with a final score of 110-34. No one could believe that the Pineys played such a good game.

In the locker room, the coach went over the statistics for the game. He told Pete, Harry, John, Phil and Stan that they scored the most points in the team's history. The five starters' scores were 8, 10, 22, 28 and 30. From the following clues, can you figure out who scored how many points?

1.   The 30 points weren't made by Pete. Everyone scored more than Pete.

2.   The 28 points weren't made by Harry, who scored two more points than Phil.

3.   Stan scored fewer points than John.

1. *Harry scored the most points— 30.*

2. *Phil scored two fewer than Harry— 28.*

3. *John scored 22.*

4. *Stan chipped in with 10 points.*

5. *Pete, of course, scored the fewest points— 8.*

Potty-pourri

Hard Luck Herman was waiting on a street corner in Philadelphia one rainy afternoon. He had no hat or umbrella, was out in the open fully exposed to the elements, and, on top of the heavy precipitation, a bus splashed him from head to foot. The amazing thing is not a single hair on his head was wet - well, not so amazing really. How come?

Hard Luck Herman was bald.

What's up Doc?

Writing this book was fun. Most fun of all was playing with your mind. This paragraph is an illustration. All is not right. Can you spot what is odd? Offhand, it looks totally ordinary, but in fact, it is not. Skill with grammar or punctuation will not show a solution to your burning curiosity. Solving it in a half hour is par, although a sharp brain could whip through it without much thought. Play fair. Nobody should assist you— particularly allowing that this is a bathroom quiz book and that using a bathroom is usually a solo act. Scan this quiz and think as hard as you can; that is how you'll know what's going on. Wit will out. Good luck!

"E", the most common letter in the English language, is completely absent from the paragraph.

Potty-pourri

What do New York State, Mexico, Illinois, Massachusetts, and Florida have in common? Hint: Certain cities make the record books.

They all have cities that have famous musical groups as namesakes: Manhattan Transfer, Tijuana Brass, Chicago, Boston, and Miami Sound Machine.

Garbledegooks

Unscramble these words for things you find in the bathroom. Fill in the blanks and write the boxed letters below for an important message to all bathroom users.

1. OBMC   [C] O M B "c" goes in space #1

2. EOWHSR   _ [ ] _ _ _ _

3. SNITCIAEPT   _ _ _ _ _ [ ] _ _ _

4. LRSACEEN   [ ] _ _ _ _ _ _ _

5. KCTSGIOSN   _ _ _ [ ] _ _ _

6. ALIN FIFL   _ _ _ _   [ ] _ _ _

7. RRAOZ   _ _ [ ] _ _

8. ECERM NESIR   _ _ _ _ _   [ ] _ _ _ _ _

9. HTOTO SPTAE   _ _ _ _ _   [ ] _ _ _ _ _

10. RTOEDADON   _ _ _ _ _ _ [ ] _ _

11. ARPHME   _ _ _ [ ] _ _

12. LWTOSE   _ _ _ [ ] _ _

13. FRATE VSAEH   _ _ _ _ [ ] _ _ _ _ _

IMPORTANT MESSAGE:

_ _ _ _ _   _ _ _   _ _ _ _ _!
1 2 3 4 5   6 7 8   9 10 11 12 13

1.   *[C]OMB.*

2.   *S[H]OWER.*

3.   *ANTIS[E]PTIC.*

4.   *[C]LEANSER.*

5.   *STOC[K]INGS.*

6.   *NAIL [F]ILE.*

7.   *RAZ[O]R.*

8.   *CREME [R]INSE.*

9.   *TOOTH [P]ASTE.*

10.   *DEODOR[A]NT.*

11.   *HAM[P]ER.*

12.   *TOW[E]LS.*

13.   *AFTE[R] SHAVE.*

IMPORTANT MESSAGE:

Check For Paper!

Phrase Craze

Try your hand at these crazy statements.

1. **Statement**
   144

2.

AS

SAS

3. Heaven
   Heaven
   Heaven
   Heaven
   Heaven
   Heaven
   Hea He's ven

4.

5. **MIND**
   matter

6.

7. PANCAKES
   PANCAKES
   PANCAKES
   PANCAKES
   PANCAKES
   PANCAKES
   PANCAKES

   COLLAR

1. *Gross understatement.*

2. *ASSASSINATE.*

3. *He's in 7th Heaven.*

4. *Ace in the hole.*

5. *Mind over matter.*

6. *Ring around the collar.*

7. *A stack of pancakes.*

Potty-pourri

What is the lowest number to be spelled with all the major vowels?

One thousand and five.

Initial Reaction

Below are listed the initials of some pretty famous movies. Can you figure out the titles and match them with the stars? If not, what have you been doing at the drive-in all these years?

1.   B C A T S K   A. John Agar

2.   R O T J   B. Karen Allen

3.   A T W I E D   C. Claudette Colbert

4.   I A M M M M W   D. Brian Keith

5.   T T O T S M   E. Katherine Ross

6.   T R A C , T R A C   F. Spencer Tracy

7.   O H M S S   G. Shirley MacLaine

8.   R O T L A   H. George Lazenby

9.   I H O N   I. Billy Dee Williams

10.   T C F T B L   J. Walter Huston

1.   *Butch Cassidy And The Sundance Kid. — E*

2.   *Return Of The Jedi. — I*

3.   *Around The World In Eighty Days. — G*

4.   *It's A Mad, Mad, Mad, Mad, World. — F*

5.   *The Treasure Of The Sierra Madre. — J*

6.   *The Russians Are Coming,
      The Russians Are Coming. — D*

7.   *On Her Majesty's Secret Service. — H*

8.   *Raiders Of The Lost Ark. — B*

9.   *It Happened One Night. — C*

10.   *The Creature From The Black Lagoon. — A*

Potty-pourri

Never the twain shall meet: Name the state that contains the westernmost point in the United States ... and the state that has the easternmost point.

Alaska and Alaska! The Aleutian Islands stretch so far west, they cross the international dateline and become east.

Brain Drain

1. A treasure ship lies at anchor in a Caribbean harbor. Pirates plan to scurry up her side under the cover of darkness and steal her booty. They approach the massive ship in a small blackened dory and notice that the rope ladder slung over the side dangles just out of reach, seven feet above the water line. The water is rising at 14 inches per hour and the highest any of the pirates can reach is five and three quarters feet. How long must the buccaneers wait before the ladder comes within reach?

2. Think of your closest friend. Now don't get upset but he, she or it can sit somewhere that you'll never be able to sit. Where is it?

3. Are 1986 dollar bills worth more than 1984 dollar bills?

4. William Tell III always had trouble living up to his forebearer's reputation and was goaded by the locals unmercifully. Finally he decided to end the taunts once and for all. Late one Oktoberfest, he strode into the local tavern and announced that he would cover any bets that said that he could not go into the woods, be blindfolded, hang up his hat, walk 200 yards and put a bullet through it. *"I may not be much good as an archer— but as a marksman. . .watch out!"* he said as he tallied up the bets. Followed by a couple of dozen concerned parties, he went into the forest, and shortly after emerged with pockets bulging, a self-satisfied smile on his face and a hole in his hat. How'd he do it?

5. It is an established fact that the great Dodger pitcher Sandy Koufax could throw a baseball with all of his might and have it stop in mid-flight and return to his glove. Although he never used it on the mound— it would have been an illegal pitch— he nevertheless demonstrated it many times in his career. What did he call this amazing feat?

1. *They'll have to wait until Davy Jones cleans out his locker. If the water level is rising, so is the ship and the ladder remains out of reach.*

2. *Your lap.*

3. *Yes, 1986 dollars are worth $2 more than 1984 dollars — and $3 more than 1983 dollars and $4 more than 1982 dollars...*

4. *He never specified where he would hang his hat so he hung it over the end of his rifle barrel.*

5. *He called it, "Throwing the ball up in the air."*

Potty-pourri

Tauren "Nick" O'Teen was a cigarette fanatic. He couldn't bear to see any tobacco go to waste. He discovered he could roll one new cigarette from every four discarded butts. How may new smokes could he fashion from the remains of a standard pack of 20?

Six and a quarter of the seventh. He could roll five cigarettes from the pack of 20 and an additional 1¼ from those five.

Boogie Woogie Bureaucrats

Bureaucrats have a language all their own. This quiz offers famous song titles and lyrics as they would be written by the government. Try to identify each, but if you find them bloated beyond all recognition, feel free to consult your accountant and/or lawyer.

1. What is the number of thoroughfares of which a male is required to make a longitudinal transit prior to being bestowed with the designation "man"?

2. It is helpful to obtain a knowledge of how to differentiate situations where A: it would be beneficial to maintain your current status; or B: economic stability in the long term would best be served by engaging in a tactical retreat.

3. SONG TITLE— Homo Sapiens endowed with the dual-x chromosome characteristic are prone to focus their energies in the recreational sector.

4. SONG TITLE— My multi-chambered blood recirculating pump has been abandoned in the geographical region abutting the southern end of the Golden Gate Bridge.

5. Is the stimulation threshold of your visual cortex exceeded by the scant number of photons available during the incipient stages of daylight as your geographical coordinates traverse Earth's Terminator?

6. SONG TITLE— Do not make inarticulate sounds of grief on my behalf, second largest country in South America.

7. SONG TITLE— Grip my person, continually restraining my movements, stimulate my limbic and glandular systems and then proceed to osculate.

8. She will experience gaiety upon gaiety upon gaiety until such time as the person who sired her removes the rapidly accelerating, streamlined vehicle from her possession.

9. I am experiencing a reverie concerning a profundity of hexagonal water crystals during yuletide.

10. A beast of burden is a beast of burden indubitably, indubitably...

1. *How many roads must a man travel down, before they call him a man?* <u>(Blowin' In The Wind.)</u>

2. *You've got to know when to hold 'em, know when to fold 'em.* <u>(The Gambler)</u>.

3. <u>Girls Just Want To Have Fun.</u>

4. <u>I Left My Heart in San Francisco.</u>

5. *Oh, say can you see. . .by the dawn's early light. . .?* <u>(Star Spangled Banner)</u>.

6. <u>Don't Cry for Me, Argentina.</u>

7. <u>Hold Me, Thrill Me, Kiss Me.</u>

8. *And she'll have fun, fun, fun, 'till her daddy takes the T-Bird away.* <u>(Fun Fun Fun)</u>.

9. *I'm dreaming of a White Christmas. . .* <u>(White Christmas)</u>.

10. *A horse is a horse, of course, of course. . .* <u>(Mr. Ed Theme)</u>.

Potty-pourri

Little Tommy had a reputation for fibbing so when he said his grandfather was only three years older than his father, nobody believed him. They should have. How is this possible?

His mother married an older man who was only three years younger than her father.

Word Squares

This quiz will test your patience if not your vocabulary. Add letters so that each column and row contains the same words.

```
M  __  __  E
A  __  __  __
__  __  N  __
__  A  __  __
```

```
T  __  __  __  T
__  __  N  __  __
__  N  __  __  X
__  C  __  __  __
__  __  __  T  __
```

```
M   A   D   E
A   R   E   A
D   E   N   S
E   A   S   E
```

```
T   O   A   S   T
O   U   N   C   E
A   N   N   E   X
S   C   E   N   T
T   E   X   T   S
```

Potty-pourri

Name three sporting events that should be popular with backward students.

Rowing, backstroke and tug of war.

Common Nouns

Let's check the elasticity of your mind! The following word groups all have a common denominator. For instance, Hound-Finn-Pie should suggest Huckleberry! If it doesn't, just skip this page and go onto something else.

1. Earth's—Fireplace—Mickey

2. Mounted—Toilet—Royal

3. Tree—Drop—Meadowlark

4. Port—Over—Out

5. Way—Great—Sided

6. Easter—Dust—Bugs

7. Foot—Masquerade—Lightning

8. Whitney—Thelma—Texas

9. Slipper—Eye—Shot

10. Used—Side—Wash

1.   *Mantle.*

2.   *Flush.*

3.   *Lemon.*

4.   *Pass.*

5.   *One.*

6.   *Bunny.*

7.   *Ball.*

8.   *Houston.*

9.   *Glass.*

10.   *Car.*

Potty-pourri

Squire Schnootzle was an obsessive groundskeeper. Every autumn day, he'd rake the leaves in the front yard into 11 big piles. He'd then rake the backyard leaves into 15 piles. At that point he'd rake them all together in the side yard. How many piles would there be in the Squire's side yard?

One.

Sum Fun

Use a little strategy to arrange numbers in the blanks so that when added either in columns or rows, they total the figure on the right of the square.

$$\begin{array}{ccc} \underline{} & \underline{} & \underline{2} \\ \underline{5} & \underline{} & \underline{} \\ \underline{} & \underline{3} & \underline{} \end{array} \quad 10$$

$$\begin{array}{cccc} \underline{} & \underline{9} & \underline{} & \underline{} \\ \underline{5} & \underline{} & \underline{} & \underline{} \\ \underline{} & \underline{} & \underline{} & \underline{2} \\ \underline{} & \underline{8} & \underline{} & \underline{} \end{array} \quad 24$$

$$\begin{array}{cccc} \underline{4} & \underline{} & \underline{} & \underline{} \\ \underline{} & \underline{9} & \underline{} & \underline{} \\ \underline{} & \underline{} & \underline{} & \underline{9} \\ \underline{} & \underline{} & \underline{6} & \underline{} \end{array} \quad 28$$

```
3   5   2
5   2   3
2   3   5
```

```
                    2   9   5   8
                    5   2   8   9
                    8   5   9   2
                    9   8   2   5
```

```
4   6   9   9
9   9   4   6
6   4   9   9
9   9   6   4
```

Potty-pourri

Starting at one and spelling succeeding numbers in sequence, how many would you have to write before using all the vowels?

One thousand.

Switcheroos

Change one letter per step and each resulting switcheroo must be an English word. No contractions, proper nouns or slang, please.

1. Switcheroo FISH to WARP in 4 steps:
    FISH - ___ - ___ - ___ - WARP

2. Switcheroo RUSH to PART in 5 steps:
    RUSH - ___ - ___ - ___ - ___ - PART

3. Switcheroo PLATE to CLAMS in 4 steps:
    PLATE - ___ - ___ - ___ - CLAMS

4. Switcheroo TURN to SITE in 6 steps:
    TURN - ___ - ___ - ___ - ___ - ___ - SITE

5. Switcheroo REAL to HAIR in 5 steps:
    REAL - ___ - ___ - ___ - ___ - HAIR

6. Switcheroo ROCK to TALC in 5 steps:
    ROCK - ___ - ___ - ___ - ___ - TALC

7. Switcheroo BELL to CAVE in 6 steps:
    BELL - ___ - ___ - ___ - ___ - ___ - CAVE

8. Switcheroo GRIPE to IRATE in 3 steps:
    GRIPE - ___ - ___ - IRATE

9. Switcheroo BRINE to TRUNK in 4 steps:
    BRINE - ___ - ___ - ___ - TRUNK

10. Switcheroo HEAVY to LENSE in 5 steps:
    HEAVY - ___ - ___ - ___ - ___ - LENSE

1. *FISH - WISH - WASH - WASP - WARP*

2. *RUSH - PUSH - PUSS - PASS - PAST - PART*

3. *PLATE - PLANE - PLANS - CLANS - CLAMS*

4. *TURN - BURN - BORN - BORE - SORE - SIRE - SITE*

5. *REAL - DEAL - DEAR - HEAR - HEIR - HAIR*

6. *ROCK - SOCK - SACK - TACK - TALK - TALC*

7. *BELL - BALL - TALL - TALE - SALE - SAVE - CAVE*

8. *GRIPE - GRAPE - GRATE - IRATE*

9. *BRINE - BRINK - DRINK - DRUNK - TRUNK*

10. *HEAVY - HEAVE - WEAVE - LEAVE - LEASE - LENSE*

Potty-pourri

Which is correct - "6 and 7 <u>is</u> 15" or "6 and 7 <u>are</u> 15"?

Neither - 6 added to 7 totals 13!

Riddle Of The Pyramid

Below are clues for words which fit into the pyramid. Start each word where the arrow points and work clockwise or counter-clockwise around the number. Two letters of each word overlap.

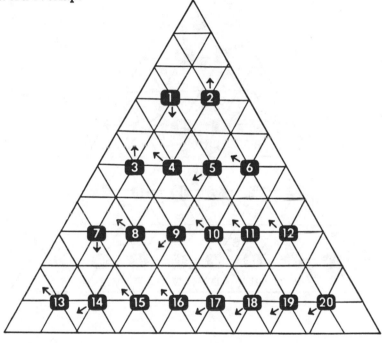

CLUES:

1. To give refuge to
2. Arousing no interest
3. Reflector
4. Cynical
5. Agile
6. Blast
7. To give in great abundance
8. Chore
9. Sickly
10. Distress
11. Comment
12. No particular pattern
13. Ill tempered
14. Not broad
15. Lusty
16. Abrupt
17. Argue
18. Innate capability
19. Close
20. Leaf through

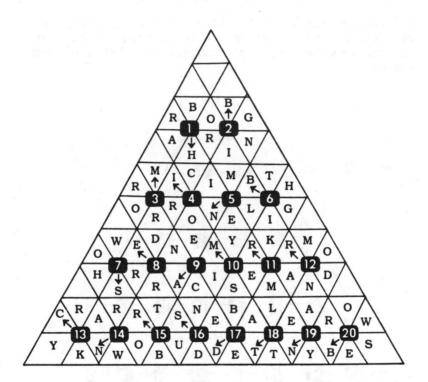

Showered With Statistics

1. On the average, Americans use ____ pounds of tooth-paste a week: A) 750,000 B) 1 million C) 3.8 million D) 50,000

2. Americans will spend ____ a month on dental floss: A) $36,000 B) $15,000 C) $30,000 D) $5,000

3. The average number of diapers changed daily across the United States is: A) 60 million B) 10 million C) 300,000 D) 150,000

4. Believe it or not, Americans import ____ bottles of drinking water from Mexico a year. A) 50,000 B) 2,500 C) 10,000 D) 210,000

5. After a month of daily baths, a typical American has used ____ gallons of water. A) 1,100 B) 500 C) 750 D) 2,000

6. Every time we flush our toilets we use ____ gallons of water. A) 1.2 B) 6.8 C) 4.6 D) 8.7

7. Weekly, ____ gallons of mouthwash are used in America. A) 72,000 B) 550,000 C) 483,000 D) 15,000

8. How long out of a busy day does the average person spend on personal care? A) 68 min. B) 75 min. C) 45 min. D) 30 min.

9. Yearly, the average man will spend ____ hours shaving. A) 100 B) 25 C) 60 D) 250

10. If the tap is left running while shaving you use ____ gallons of water. A) 7-9 B) 3-5 C) 1-3 D) 2-6

1.   C.

2.   A.

3.   A.

4.   D.

5.   A.

6.   B.

7.   A.

8.   A.

9.   C.

10. B.

Potty-pourri

The Interplanetary Tribunal has found you guilty of indecent exposure for "mooning". Klatu, the High Commissioner, has sentenced you to a year at hard labor but given you your choice of penal colonies. Assuming similar accommodations, which planet's hoosegow should you select?

Mercury - since it has the smallest orbit, it has the shortest year. You'd be sprung in about three months.

A Cipher Sore Eyes. . .
(a Crypto Joke)

DEU WUXSJOZ QA H XUKCJO
OUUV WJDDQAW POJZZJP:

WUXSJO UAJ -

"BJN SOJP, BUE XUAW BHTJ NUY MJJA EJHOQAW H
WQOPXJ?"

WUXSJO DEU -

"JTJO ZQAKJ VN EQSJ SUYAP QD QA DBJ
WXUTJ KUVLHODVJAD US VN KHO!"

TWO GOLFERS IN A LOCKER ROOM GETTING DRESSED:

GOLFER ONE -

"HEY FRED, HOW LONG HAVE YOU BEEN WEARING A
GIRDLE?"

GOLFER TWO -

"EVER SINCE MY WIFE FOUND IT IN THE GLOVE
COMPARTMENT OF MY CAR!"

Potty-pourri

Time for a surprise history quiz. What was the name
of the vessel that had that famous tussle with the
Monitor during the Civil War?

*Yes, Virginia. It used to be called
the Merrimack but when the South captured it, it
was renamed the Virginia.*

Insert A Letter

Every letter of the alphabet fits somewhere into the blanks below - and if it is in the right place, it will complete a six or more letter word. No time limit-except for when pins and needles set in. . .

1. P J L S P ___ A S T I C
2. O R L M B ___ P A S S P
3. B G O P U ___ P O R T A
4. Q U R N A ___ O T T L E
5. N Z G R A ___ I T Y D S
6. D E B A S ___ M P L B J
7. A Γ B L I ___ P O S E R
8. G E R E L ___ P S E Z A
9. L I M B U ___ Z S A W B
10. Q U R Z L ___ E S T E R
11. P A B D L ___ Y A L T Y
12. F O L L O ___ H M R I J
13. L U R C E ___ C I T E R
14. B C R U M ___ L E P S N
15. M O N N E ___ T R A L A
16. O W N R S ___ G N O R E
17. B E X R I ___ A W D L E
18. A S K I N ___ L I N E S
19. Y U L A R ___ E N Y I P
20. T E L J U ___ G L E P S
21. A T T A C ___ I S T O L
22. M A F C U ___ U A I N T
23. R U C K U ___ P O I N E
24. M O T I G ___ O N G U E
25. H E M I S ___ A P P E Y
26. A G V B D ___ A T H E R

Answers

1. *L - Plastic.*
2. *Y - Bypass.*
3. *R - Purport.*
4. *B - Bottle.*
5. *V - Gravity.*
6. *E - Debase.*
7. *M - Impose.*
8. *A - Relapse.*
9. *Z - Buzzsaw.*
10. *J - Jester.*
11. *O - Loyalty.*
12. *W - Follow.*
13. *X - Excite.*
14. *P - Crumple.*
15. *U - Neutral.*
16. *I - Ignore.*
17. *D - Dawdle.*
18. *G - Asking.*
19. *C - Larceny.*
20. *N - Jungle.*
21. *K - Attack.*
22. *Q - Quaint.*
23. *S - Ruckus.*
24. *T - Tongue.*
25. *H - Mishap.*
26. *F - Father.*

Brain Drain

1. A cubic foot of soil weighs 47 lbs., 3 ozs. What then is the total weight of soil in a hole one meter by four meters by three meters?

2. Your car is parked facing north on North Street, so named because it runs north and south. You jump in the car and start driving along the perfectly straight thoroughfare. In only two minutes time, you are a mile south of your starting point. What happened?

3. Little Johnny has gone through his Terrible Two's, Torturous Three's and is now into his Ferocious Four's. One evening, when you are bringing your boss home for dinner, Johnny goes to the second floor window and drops an ordinary, raw chicken egg over the cement driveway. Amazingly, the egg misses your boss <u>and</u> although it falls nine feet, it doesn't break. How come?

4. Your precious little Fluffy gives birth to four female kittens, each of which has one brother. What is your house's total feline population?

5. You are deep in the wilderness high on the flank of a snow-capped mountain peak. Night is closing in and the temperature is plummeting. You've got to make camp. Even in the strong wind, you can hear your stomach growling as you pitch your dome-type tent and then, trouble. You have only one match and your equipment includes a kerosene lantern, a butane cook stove and a gasoline heater. Which should you light first?

1. *0 - there's no dirt in a hole!*

2. *You've been driving in reverse!*

3. *The second floor window is ten feet high - the egg hadn't hit the ground yet!*

4. *6—The female kittens share a common brother!*

5. *The match!*

Potty-pourri

Dog breeder Kathy Keller has 12 spaniels, 4 poodles and 7 sheepdogs. How many of Kelly's dogs can say they are the same breed as another dog at the same kennel?

None - dogs can't talk.

Common Nouns

Here's a word association workout for you. Flex your mental muscles and determine the common denominator of the word groups below.

1. Mug - Pot - Bean

2. Bulletin - Diving - Black

3. Car - Air - Authority

4. Peel - Juice - Bowl

5. Salad - Head - Mash

6. Toll - Phone - Ticket

7. Saw - Race - Work

8. Gun - Bottle - Baseball

9. Flower - Club - Vegetable

10. Hog - Country - Sign

1. *Coffee.*

2. *Board.*

3. *Port.*

4. *Orange.*

5. *Potato.*

6. *Booth.*

7. *Horse.*

8. *Cap.*

9. *Garden.*

10. *Road.*

Potty-pourri

Here's a good "bar bet" puzzle: An ice cube floats in a partially filled glass of water and your job is to remove it with a piece of string. Without touching the cube or making a loop in the string, how can you lift out the ice?

Allow the string to touch the cube, then sprinkle a pinch of salt on it. The ice will melt, then re-freeze, attaching the string.

Phrase Craze

More phrases to drive you crazy!

1. MACKEREL

2. person   ality

3. The Weather
   —————————
   Feeling

4. one   another
   one   another
   one   another
   one   another
   one   another
   one   another

5. TH_{SINGING}AIN

6. ground
   —————————
   railroad

7. CHORUSCHORUSCHORUSCHORUSCHORUS

1.   *Holy Mackerel.*

2.   *Split personality.*

3.   *Feeling under the weather.*

4.   *6 of one and half dozen of another.*

5.   *Singing in the Rain.*

6.   *Underground railroad.*

7.   *A Chorus Line.*

Potty-pourri

Peter the Possum was smarter than your average marsupial. One day he was waddling along a railroad track and he heard the whistle of an approaching express. He immediately charged <u>towards</u> the train at top speed. If he was so smart, why did he do it?

He was crossing a very high, very narrow railroad bridge when he heard the whistle. As he was almost across, he ran toward the train so he could get off the bridge and out of its way before it arrived.

Giving Your Right Arm

At first glance, this quiz may seem disarmingly simple but there's no 'arm in trying. Each clue suggests a word or phrase that contains some form of "arm". For extra fun, try it with one arm tied behind your back.

1. Police reach _____.

2. Bicarb _____.

3. Family crest _____.

4. It's a gamble _____.

5. Cure for atomic-ache _____.

6. Archie's favorite furniture _____.

7. Physically persuasive _____.

8. Hand to hand combat _____.

9. It's a pistol _____.

10. High charge _____.

1.   *Long arm of the law.*

2.   *Arm and Hammer.*

3.   *Coat of arms.*

4.   *One-armed bandit.*

5.   *Arms talks, arms reduction, etc.*

6.   *Armchair.*

7.   *Twisting your arm, strongarm tactics.*

8.   *Arm wrestling.*

9.   *Side arm.*

10.   *Costs an arm and a leg.*

Potty-pourri

During the course of their exploration, Lewis and Clark passed through the little trapping outpost called Nowhere. When they were about twenty miles from Nowhere they came to a point where several trails crossed. They wanted to go to the the Great Swamp but the signpost had been chopped down by a woodpecker. None of the party knew the way but then they came up with the solution. What was it?

They placed the signpost back in the ground with the proper arrow pointed to Nowhere. All the other arrows would then be oriented correctly.

Title Tidbits

The pop music world has always loved abbreviations. "Pop" itself, is an abbreviation for "popular." Rock 'n' Roll is now just Rock, or simply R&R. MTV, RPM, R&B. . .the list goes on and on. It seems only natural then that the song titles themselves should be abbreviated. See if you can figure out the following abbreviated song titles and then match each with the correct performer(s).

1.	I B T W Y P D B	A.	Little Richard
2.	H M, T M, K M	B.	Tommy Edwards
3.	H A H, H M B	C.	Beatles
4.	I A I T G	D.	Percy Sledge
5.	C H F I L W Y	E.	The Hollies
6.	G G M M	F.	Jan & Dean
7.	W A M L A W	G.	Brian Hyland
8.	I C G N S	H.	Mel Carter
9.	L I T S W D	I.	Rolling Stones
10.	L O L F P	J.	Elvis

1. *Itsy Bitsy Teenie Weenie Yellow Polka Dot Bikini - G.*

2. *Hold Me, Thrill Me, Kiss Me - H.*

3. *He Ain't Heavy, He's My Brother - E.*

4. *It's All in the Game - B.*

5. *Can't Help Falling in Love With You - J.*

6. *Good, Golly, Miss Molly - A.*

7. *When a Man Loves a Woman - D.*

8. *I Can't Get No Satisfaction - I.*

9. *Lucy in the Sky with Diamonds - C.*

10. *The Little Old Lady (from Pasadena) - F.*

The Bathroom Library

THE BATHROOM SPORTS QUIZ BOOK
THE BATHROOM ENTERTAINMENT BOOK
THE BATHROOM TRIVIA BOOK
THE BATHROOM DIGEST
THE BATHROOM CROSSWORD
PUZZLE BOOK
THE BATHROOM GUEST BOOK
THE BATHROOM GAME BOOK
THE BATHROOM INSPIRATION BOOK

For further information, write to:
Red-Letter Press, Inc.
P.O. Box 393
Saddle River, N.J. 07458